HERCULES
THE TWELVE LABOURS

A GREEK MYTH

GRAPHIC UNIVERSE™

STORY BY PAUL STORRIE

PENCILS BY STEVE KURTH

INKS BY BARBARA SCHULZ

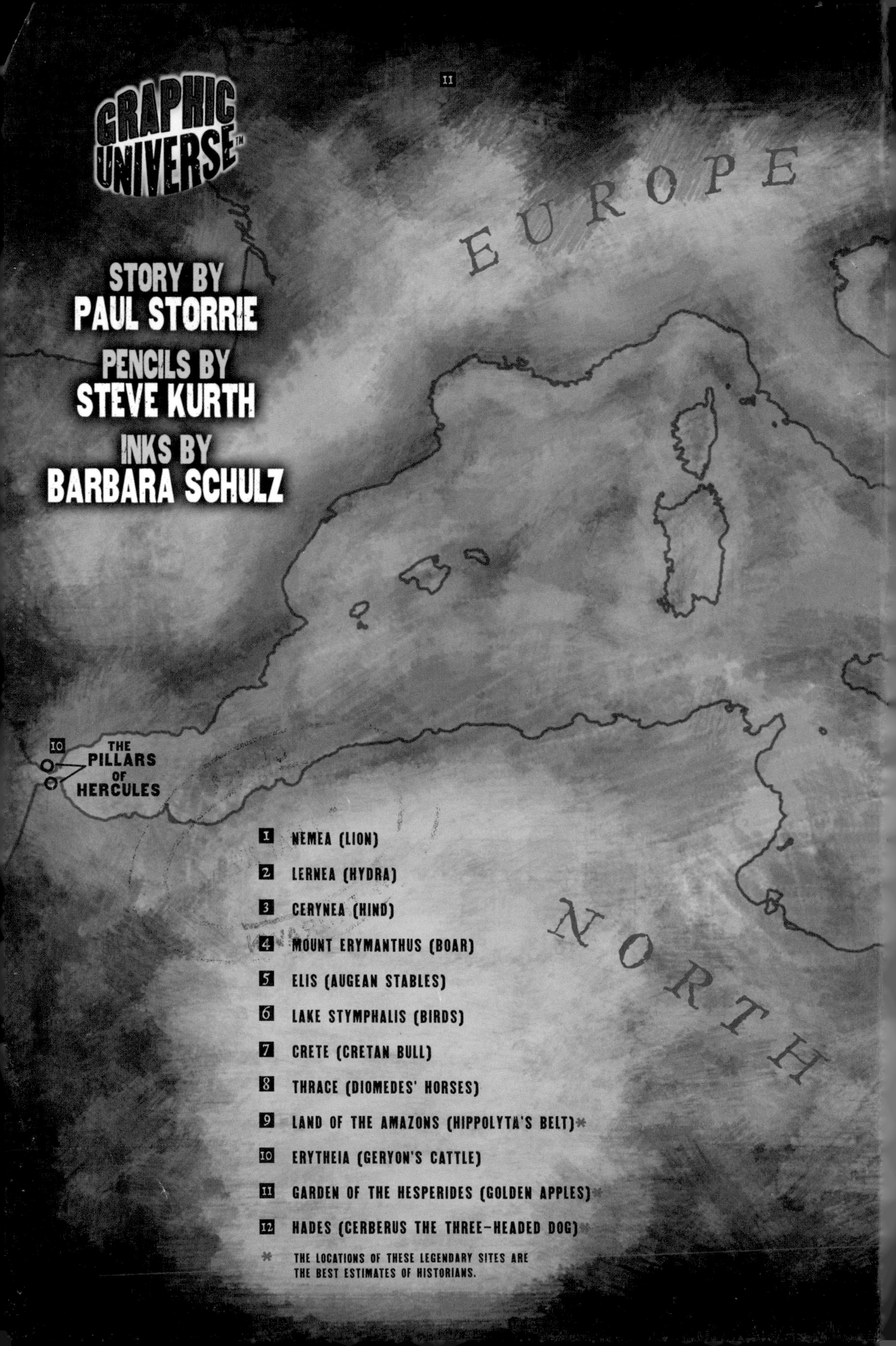

EUROPE

II

THE PILLARS OF HERCULES

10

NORTH

✳ THE LOCATIONS OF THESE LEGENDARY SITES ARE THE BEST ESTIMATES OF HISTORIANS.

HERCULES

THE TWELVE LABOURS

A GREEK MYTH

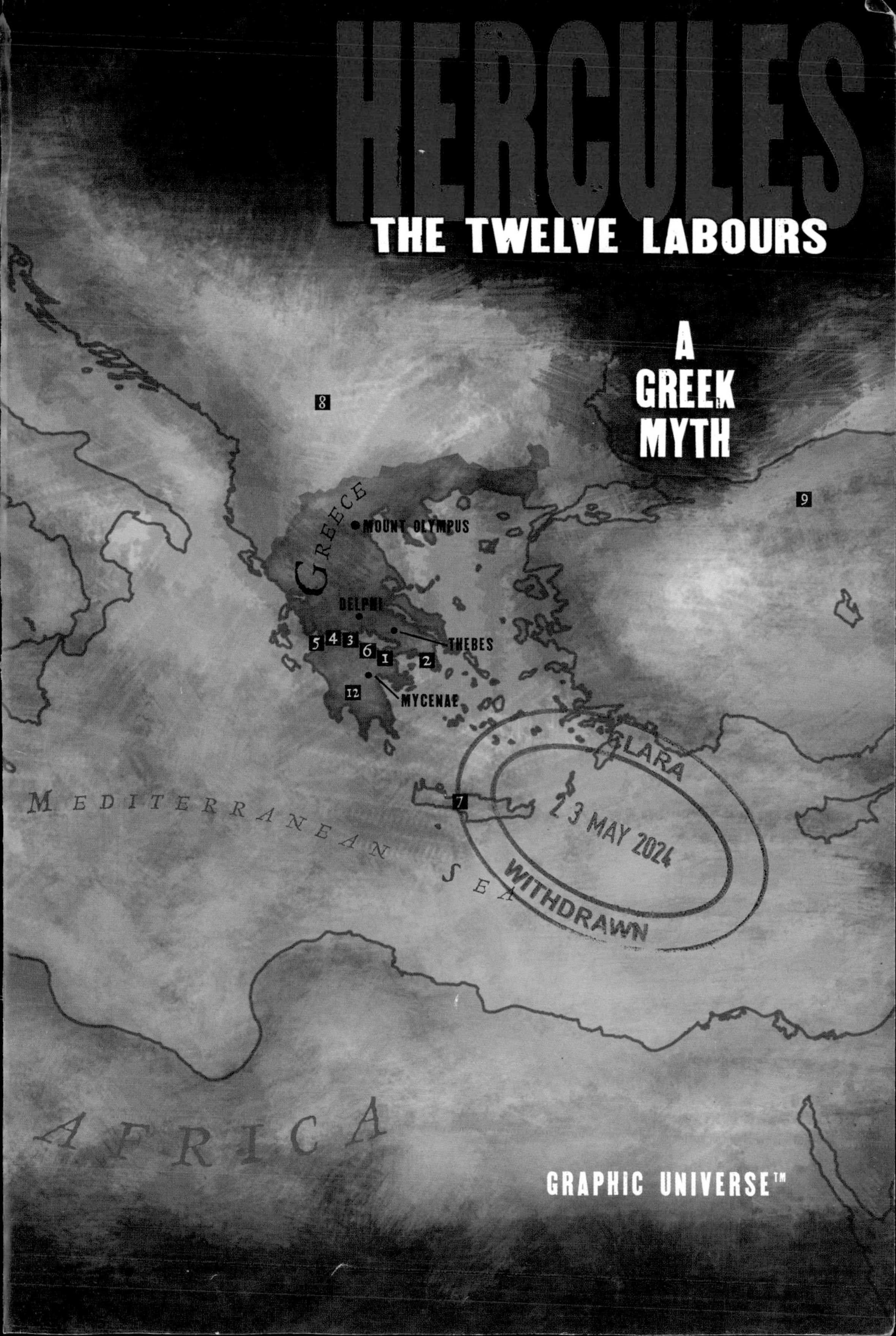

GREECE

●MOUNT OLYMPUS

DELPHI

THEBES

MYCENAE

5 4 3 6 1 2

12

8

9

7

M E D I T E R R A N E A N   S E A

A F R I C A

CLARA
3 MAY 2024
WITHDRAWN

GRAPHIC UNIVERSE™

The character Hercules may or may not have been based on an actual person. Regardless, the stories of his great feats of strength, courage and resourcefulness are among the most famous Greek legends. The Greeks called their greatest hero Herakles. But the Romans knew him as Hercules. This latter title has come down through the ages as the most popular name for this larger-than-life figure. To create the story of Hercules' Twelve Labours, author Paul Storrie relied heavily on both Thomas Bulfinch's *The Age of Fable*, first published in 1859, and Edith Hamilton's *Mythology*, first published in 1942. Both of these drew their material from the work of ancient poets such as Ovid and Virgil. Artist Steve Kurth used numerous historical and traditional sources to give the art an authentic feel, from the classical Greek architecture to the clothing, weapons and armour worn by the characters.

STORY BY PAUL STORRIE

PENCILS BY STEVE KURTH
INKS BY BARBARA SCHULZ

COLOURING BY HI-FI DESIGN

LETTERING BY BILL HAUSER

Copyright © 2007 by Lerner Publishing Group, Inc.

Graphic Universe™ is a trademark of Lerner Publishing Group, Inc.

This book was first published in the USA in 2007. First published in the UK in 2008 by Lerner Books, Dalton House, 60 Windsor Avenue, London, SW19 2RR

Website address: www.lernerbooks.co.uk

This edition was updated and edited for UK publication by Discovery Books Ltd., Unit 3, 37 Watling Street, Leintwardine, Shropshire, SY7 0LW

British Library Cataloguing in Publication Data

Storrie, Paul D.
    Hercules : the twelve labours. - (Graphic myths and legends series)
    1. Heracles (Greek mythology) - Comic books, strips, etc. - Juvenile fiction 2. Children's stories - Comic books, strips, etc.
    I. Title II. Kurth, Steve
    741.5

TABLE OF CONTENTS

THE LEGEND BEGINS

LONG AGO, IN THE FAR-OFF LAND OF GREECE, THERE LIVED A HERO NAMED **HERCULES**. THERE HAS NEVER BEEN A MAN AS STRONG, BEFORE OR SINCE.

HIS MOTHER WAS **ALCMENA**, A **MORTAL**, BUT HIS FATHER WAS **ZEUS**, THE KING OF THE **GODS**.

THE **GODDESS HERA** WAS JEALOUS THAT **ZEUS**, HER HUSBAND, LOVED A **MORTAL** WOMAN. BECAUSE OF THAT, SHE HATED **HERCULES**.

HERCULES WAS RAISED IN THE CITY OF *THEBES*, ALONG WITH HIS HALF BROTHER, *IPHICLES*.

EACH NIGHT, *ALCMENA* WOULD PUT HER SONS TO BED IN A GREAT *BRONZE SHIELD* THAT SERVED AS THEIR CRIB.

ONE NIGHT, HERA SENT TWO SERPENTS TO SLAY THE SLEEPING HERCULES, NOT CARING THAT HIS BROTHER WAS IN DANGER TOO.

BUT *ZEUS* WATCHED OVER HIS SON AND SENT A *BRIGHT LIGHT* TO WAKE HIM.

EVEN AS A *CHILD*, HE WAS *STRONG* ENOUGH TO SAVE HIS BROTHER AND HIMSELF.

SON OF *ZEUS*, YOU MUST GO TO YOUR COUSIN, *KING EURYSTHEUS* OF *MYCENAE*, AND PUT YOURSELF IN HIS SERVICE.

THIS IS THE WILL OF THE GODS.

WHEN HE WAS A GROWN MAN, HE WENT TO THE *ORACLE AT DELPHI*, WHO GAVE MESSAGES FROM THE GODS, TO LEARN WHAT HE SHOULD DO WITH HIS GREAT GIFT OF *STRENGTH*.

THOUGH *HERCULES* COULD NOT SEE HER, IT WAS THE *GODDESS HERA* WHO SPOKE THROUGH THE *ORACLE* THAT DAY.

...STRIKE YOU DOWN!

PERHAPS NOT.

IF WEAPONS FAIL...

MY STRENGTH WILL HAVE TO BE ENOUGH!

10

HAS THERE BEEN NO WORD?

SURELY THE BEAST HAS DEVOURED HIM BY NOW.

NO WORD YET MY KING, BUT...

EURYSTHEUS!

AAAHHH!

HA, HA, HA! HA!

NO NEED FOR FEAR, COUSIN!

DO YOU LIKE MY NEW CLOAK? IT WAS NOT EASY TO GET.

THE KING WAS ASHAMED THAT THE SIGHT OF HERCULES IN THE LION'S SKIN HAD FRIGHTENED HIM. HE WANTED TO MAKE HERCULES *PAY* FOR THAT EMBARRASSMENT.

YES, VERY NICE. PERHAPS IT WILL HELP PROTECT YOU DURING YOUR NEXT TASK.

IN THE SWAMPS OF LERNEA, THERE LIVES A BEAST CALLED THE HYDRA...

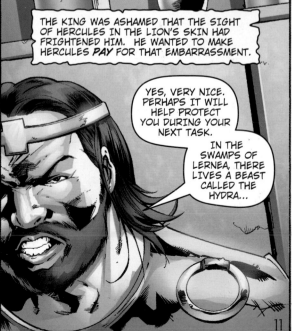

11

TO BEGIN HIS **SECOND LABOUR** AS SOON AS POSSIBLE, HERCULES ASKED HIS NEPHEW **IOLAUS** TO TAKE HIM TO LERNEA BY CHARIOT. IOLAUS WAS THE SON OF **IPHICLES**, HERCULES' HALF BROTHER.

MUCH BETTER. HARD TO FIGHT WHAT YOU CAN BARELY SEE.

IS IT TRUE THAT THIS HYDRA HAS NINE HEADS, HERCULES? AND THAT ONE OF THE HEADS CANNOT BE KILLED?

SO EURYSTHEUS TELLS ME. AND THAT ITS BLOOD IS POISON.

I WONDER IF THERE WAS ANYTHING HE DECIDED NOT TO TELL?

LET'S SEE IF WE CAN ROUSE THE BEAST.

HISSSSSSSSSSSSSSSSSSSSSSSSSSSSSSSSSSSSSSSSSS

THIS CANNOT BE!

EACH HEAD I DESTROY, TWO TAKE ITS PLACE!

IOLAUS! GRAB A BRANCH FROM THE FIRE.

HURRY!

IOLAUS?

I UNDERSTAND!

TSSSSS!

WELL DONE! WE MAY WIN OUT AFTER ALL!

THE GRIM BATTLE CONTINUED AS DAYLIGHT FADED. THEN, ONLY ONE HEAD REMAINED. THE IMMORTAL ONE.

NOW, LET IT END!

AFTER HE STRUCK OFF THE IMMORTAL HEAD, HERCULES BURIED IT BENEATH A ROCK. THEN HE AND IOLAUS PREPARED TO RETURN TO MYCENAE.

IF THIS MONSTER'S BLOOD IS POISON, THESE ARROWS MAY PROVE USEFUL IN MY OTHER LABOURS.

WHAT WERE YOU *THINKING*, HERCULES? TO TAKE A BOY HIS AGE INTO SUCH DANGER!

BESIDES, THE GODS' WISH WAS FOR *YOU* TO SERVE ME, NOT HAVE *IOLAUS* PERFORM YOUR LABOURS FOR YOU!

HE ALREADY HAS A WARRIOR'S *COURAGE*. NOW HE MUST LEARN...

NO MATTER. YOUR *THIRD LABOUR* WILL BE LESS CHALLENGING, SO YOU WILL HAVE NO NEED OF *HELP*.

I WANT YOU TO FETCH ME THE CERYNEAN HIND. AMAZING CREATURE -- IT HAS HORNS OF *GOLD!*

YOU WANT ME TO BRING YOU A DEER? HARDLY A LABOUR TO MATCH MY PROWESS.

THIS SHOULD NOT TAKE LONG.

I ADMIT, I DO NOT UNDERSTAND EITHER. A HIND?

ONE SACRED TO THE MOON GODDESS *ARTEMIS.* IF HE KILLS IT, SHE WILL *SURELY* PUNISH HIM.

BUT YOU TOLD HIM...

I TOLD HIM TO *FETCH* THE ANIMAL, NOT HARM IT.

AH, YES. VERY CLEVER INDEED.

15

MONTHS LATER, HERCULES RETURNED.

EURYSTHEUS!

HERE IT IS!

HOW...? WHAT ABOUT...?

LONG MONTHS I TRACKED AND CHASED HER. SHE WAS FAST AND CLEVER. I THOUGHT I MIGHT NEVER CATCH HER.

FINALLY, I USED AN *ARROW* TO BRING HER DOWN.

THEN, AS I MADE MY WAY BACK, ARTEMIS APPEARED BEFORE ME!

SEEMS THIS GOLDEN-HORNED CREATURE IS A FAVOURITE OF HERS.

SHE WAS ANGRY JUST *THINKING* THAT I HAD HURT IT.

HOW IS IT SHE LET YOU PASS, UNHINDERED AND UNHARMED?

LUCKY FOR ME, I HAD *NOT* HURT IT.

I KNEW SUCH A MAGNIFICENT CREATURE MUST BE TOUCHED BY THE GODS.

BUT YOU SAID...

THAT I BROUGHT IT DOWN WITH AN ARROW. I SHOT BETWEEN ITS LEGS AND TRIPPED IT. THEN I CAUGHT IT BEFORE IT COULD RUN.

SINCE IT WAS NOT HURT, ARTEMIS LET ME FINISH MY TASK. I HAD TO PROMISE TO LET IT GO. NOW I HAVE!

LATER...

WHAT TROUBLES YOU, MY KING?

Bah. IT IS ONLY A MATTER OF TIME BEFORE HERCULES RETURNS FROM HIS *FOURTH LABOUR.*

SLAYING THE ERYMANTHEAN BOAR WILL BE NO CHALLENGE TO HIM.

PERHAPS NOT, MY KING.

BUT THE FEARSOME BOAR HAS BEEN TERRORIZING THOSE WHO LIVE NEAR MOUNT ERYMANTHUS.

AT LEAST IT WILL NO LONGER HURT YOUR PEOPLE.

TRUE. I JUST WISH I COULD THINK OF SOME OTHER LABOUR TO...

KING EURYSTHEUS!

HERCULES IS COMING!

IT IS AMAZING, MY KING.

HE CHASED THE BEAST UP AND DOWN THE MOUNTAINSIDE FOR DAYS.

FINALLY, HE DROVE IT INTO A SNOWBANK NEAR THE PEAK.

THEN HE WAITED UNTIL IT WAS EXHAUSTED FROM STRUGGLING TO GET FREE!

EXHAUSTED?!? THEN IT IS STILL *ALIVE*?!?

Y-YES, MY KING.

AND HE IS *BRINGING* IT *HERE*?

YES, MY KING.

GO! RUN! TELL HERCULES THAT FROM NOW ON HE SHOULD SHOW THE PROOF OF HIS LABOURS TO THE GUARD CAPTAIN AT THE GATE.

NOT TO ME, YOU UNDERSTAND? *NOT TO ME!*

17

GREAT CHALLENGES

King Eurystheus was ashamed at being so frightened about the boar. He blamed Hercules and wanted to embarrass his cousin just as much.

For the *FIFTH LABOUR*, Eurystheus sent Hercules to clean out the stables of King Augeas in a single day, a task as impossible as it was disgusting.

THERE THEY ARE -- THE STABLES THAT YOU AGREED TO CLEAN!

Ugh! BY THE SMELL, I CAN TELL NO ONE HAS TOUCHED THEM IN *YEARS*.

I WILL DO IT, BUT YOU MUST GIVE ME ONE OF EVERY TEN ANIMALS IN RETURN.

HA! WHY NOT?

TELL ME, PHYLEUS, MY SON, DO YOU THINK HE'LL MANAGE IT?

I DON'T KNOW, FATHER.

EVEN WITH THE HUNDREDS OF ANIMALS OUT GRAZING IN THE FIELDS, HERCULES REALIZED THAT HE COULD NEVER *CLEAN* OUT THE STABLES IN ONE DAY.

THOOM!

HE HAD TO FIND ANOTHER WAY.

HE DECIDED TO LET THE TWO NEARBY RIVERS DO THE WORK FOR HIM.

THE TWO CHANNELS MET JUST OUTSIDE THE STABLE WALL.

RRRRUUMMMBBBLLLE

POW!

HERCULES LEAPT TO THE TOP OF THE WALL TO WATCH THE MARVELOUS SIGHT.

AFTER A FEW HOURS, HERCULES BLOCKED THE TRENCHES CLOSE TO THE RIVERS, AND THE WATERS DRAINED AWAY.

ARE YOU **INSANE?!?**

I HAVE DONE WHAT I SAID I WOULD DO. TIME TO PAY UP!

NO, IT IS NOT!

I HAVE LEARNED THAT YOU DID THIS AT THE BIDDING OF KING EURYSTHEUS AND THAT THE GODS TOLD YOU TO SERVE HIM. YOU HAD NO RIGHT TO ASK FOR PAYMENT!

WHATEVER HIS REASON, YOU PROMISED HIM THE ANIMALS, FATHER...

WHAT? YOU TAKE **HIS** SIDE?

GET OUT OF MY KINGDOM, THE PAIR OF YOU! COUNT YOURSELVES **LUCKY** TO LEAVE WITH YOUR **LIVES!**

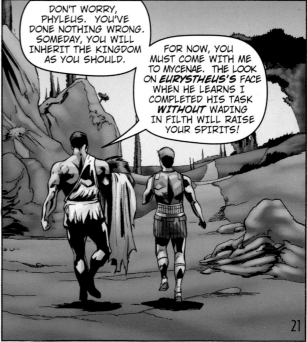

DON'T WORRY, PHYLEUS. YOU'VE DONE NOTHING WRONG. SOMEDAY, YOU WILL INHERIT THE KINGDOM AS YOU SHOULD.

FOR NOW, YOU MUST COME WITH ME TO MYCENAE. THE LOOK ON **EURYSTHEUS'S** FACE WHEN HE LEARNS I COMPLETED HIS TASK **WITHOUT** WADING IN FILTH WILL RAISE YOUR SPIRITS!

21

HERCULES WAS RIGHT ABOUT HIS COUSIN'S DISAPPOINTMENT. HE WAS NOT SURPRISED WHEN THE KING SENT HIM TO HIS *SIXTH LABOUR* RIGHT AWAY, BUT HE WAS PUZZLED BY THE TASK.

KING EURYSTHEUS SENT HIM TO THE STYMPHALIAN LAKE TO CHASE AWAY SOME *BIRDS* THAT WERE BOTHERING THE FARMERS THERE. IT SEEMED TOO EASY.

WHEN HE ARRIVED, THE LAKESHORE LOOKED PEACEFUL.

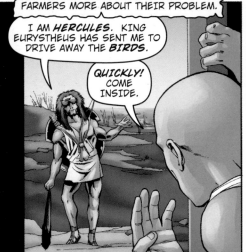

HE DECIDED TO ASK ONE OF THE FARMERS MORE ABOUT THEIR PROBLEM.

I AM *HERCULES*. KING EURYSTHEUS HAS SENT ME TO DRIVE AWAY THE *BIRDS*.

QUICKLY! COME INSIDE.

WHY ARE YOUR ANIMALS IN HERE, INSTEAD OF THE PEN?

NOTHING IS SAFE OUTSIDE! THE BIRDS WOULD GET THEM.

THEY ARE MONSTERS! THEIR CLAWS AND BEAKS ARE MADE OF BRASS.

THEIR FEATHERS SHINE LIKE BRONZE AND DROP FROM THE SKY LIKE ARROWS!

WHAT THEY KILL, THEY DRAG AWAY TO EAT.

IT SEEMS EURYSTHEUS FORGOT TO TELL ME THE CREATURES WERE SO FIERCE.

NO MATTER. I WILL DRIVE THEM OFF.

NO! STAY!

FEAR NOT! YOUR WARNINGS SHOULD KEEP ME SAFE.

THIS SHOULD ROUSE THEM.

CLANG! CLANG! CLANG! CLANG! CLANG!

AH! HERE THEY COME.

CLANG! CLANG! CLANG!

TAK TAK TAK-TAK TAK TAK TAK TAK TAK TAK TAK TAK TAK TAK

ARRGH!

ENOUGH OF THIS!

23

KREEE!

BECAUSE OF THE HYDRA'S BLOOD ON THE ARROWS, A SCRATCH WAS ENOUGH TO KILL.

Thump

Thump

HERCULES FIRED ARROW AFTER ARROW.

KREEE!

HIS ONLY FEAR WAS THAT HE WOULD NOT HAVE ENOUGH.

EVENTUALLY, THE LAST FEW BIRDS FLEW OFF. WHAT HAPPENED TO THEM, NO ONE KNOWS, BUT THEY NEVER RETURNED TO THE STYMPHALIAN LAKE AGAIN.

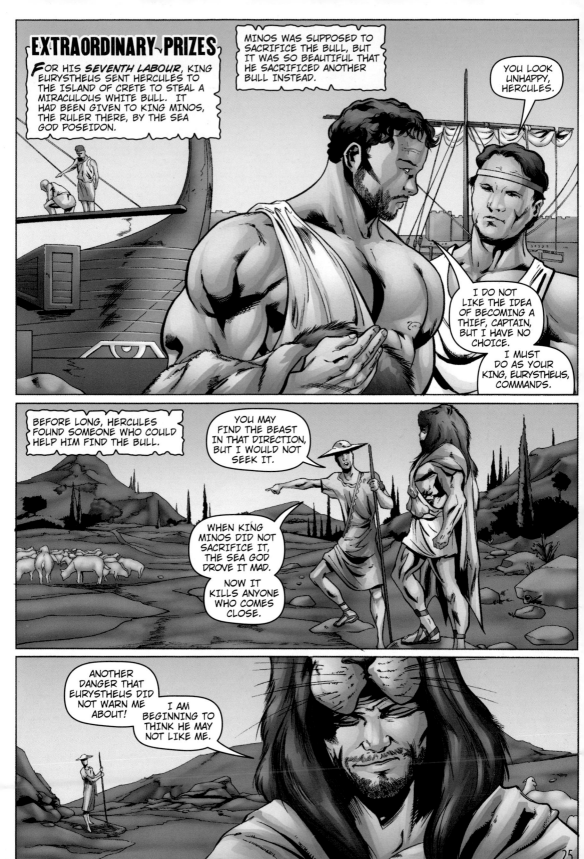

EXTRAORDINARY PRIZES

FOR HIS **SEVENTH LABOUR**, KING EURYSTHEUS SENT HERCULES TO THE ISLAND OF CRETE TO STEAL A MIRACULOUS WHITE BULL. IT HAD BEEN GIVEN TO KING MINOS, THE RULER THERE, BY THE SEA GOD POSEIDON.

MINOS WAS SUPPOSED TO SACRIFICE THE BULL, BUT IT WAS SO BEAUTIFUL THAT HE SACRIFICED ANOTHER BULL INSTEAD.

YOU LOOK UNHAPPY, HERCULES.

I DO NOT LIKE THE IDEA OF BECOMING A THIEF, CAPTAIN, BUT I HAVE NO CHOICE.

I MUST DO AS YOUR KING, EURYSTHEUS, COMMANDS.

BEFORE LONG, HERCULES FOUND SOMEONE WHO COULD HELP HIM FIND THE BULL.

YOU MAY FIND THE BEAST IN THAT DIRECTION, BUT I WOULD NOT SEEK IT.

WHEN KING MINOS DID NOT SACRIFICE IT, THE SEA GOD DROVE IT MAD.

NOW IT KILLS ANYONE WHO COMES CLOSE.

ANOTHER DANGER THAT EURYSTHEUS DID NOT WARN ME ABOUT!

I AM BEGINNING TO THINK HE MAY NOT LIKE ME.

SOON, HERCULES FOUND THE BULL.

MRRRUUUH!

THEY STRUGGLED FOR HOURS.

FINALLY, THE CREATURE BEGAN TO TIRE.

THE BULL HIT THE GROUND SO HARD THAT IT WAS DAZED.

Ugh! THANK THE GODS I DO NOT HAVE TO FIGHT YOU ALL THE WAY BACK TO THE SHIP!

AFTER HERCULES DELIVERED THE WHITE BULL OF CRETE, KING EURYSTHEUS SENT HIM TO THRACE TO STEAL AWAY A PAIR OF PRIZE MARES OWNED BY KING DIOMEDES. HIS *EIGHTH LABOUR* SOUNDED EASY ENOUGH, BUT HERCULES HAD LEARNED TO EXPECT UNPLEASANT SURPRISES.

GREETINGS, FRIEND!

ARE THESE THE STABLES OF KING DIOMEDES?

YES, THEY ARE. YOU MUST NOT BE FROM THRACE. ALL THE LOCALS STAY AWAY.

WHY IS THAT? I HEAR THE MARES THAT DRAW THE KING'S CHARIOT ARE AMAZING CREATURES.

SO YOU CAME TO SEE THEM?

INDEED I DID.

SORRY, BUT THAT WOULD NOT BE SAFE. TRUST ME, I AM THEIR TRAINER.

YOU SOUND UNHAPPY ABOUT IT.

THE KING LIKES THEM TRAINED AND FED A CERTAIN WAY. IT MAKES THEM DANGEROUS.

FOR EXAMPLE, MOST HORSES LIKE TO BE PETTED. THESE WOULD HAPPILY GNAW YOUR HAND OFF.

GOOD TO KNOW.

TO BE HONEST, I WAS SENT HERE TO STEAL THEM.

I DID NOT LIKE THE IDEA, BUT IT SOUNDS LIKE DIOMEDES IS NOT FIT TO OWN THEM. I HOPE YOU WILL NOT TRY TO STOP ME.

I DOUBT I COULD, EVEN IF I WANTED TO. GOOD LUCK TO YOU. THEY WILL BE BETTER OFF AWAY FROM HERE.

27

THEY CAN HAVE YOU WHEN I FINISH!

TO DEFEND HIMSELF, HERCULES WAS FORCED TO RELEASE THE MARES.

No.

NOOOoooohhhhooooooo!

SORRY. HE STRUCK ME WHEN I TRIED TO STOP HIM.

NO MATTER. IN THE END, HE GOT WHAT HE DESERVED.

PERHAPS. WILL EURYSTHEUS TREAT THEM BETTER?

I WILL TELL HIM WHAT HAPPENED TO DIOMEDES. IF I KNOW EURYSTHEUS, HE WILL BE TOO *FRIGHTENED* TO BE *CRUEL* TO THEM.

WHAT NOW? HERCULES HAS SUCCEEDED AT EVERY TASK I GAVE HIM. NOTHING HURTS HIM. NOTHING SHAMES HIM.

BUT WHAT...

YES! CALL FOR HERCULES!

FOR THE **NINTH LABOUR**, KING EURYSTHEUS SENT HERCULES TO THE LAND OF THE AMAZONS. THE AMAZONS WERE A NATION OF FIERCE WARRIOR WOMEN WHO COULD FIGHT AS WELL AS ANY MAN. THE BRAVEST OF THEM, HIPPOLYTA, WAS THEIR QUEEN.

WHAT IS YOUR PURPOSE HERE?

I MUST SPEAK WITH HIPPOLYTA.

WHETHER YOU DO OR NOT WILL BE UP TO THE **QUEEN.**

I WILL BRING HER YOUR REQUEST.

UNTIL I RETURN, STAY ON YOUR SHIP.

IF YOU TRY TO COME ON LAND, MY COMRADES WILL STOP YOU.

A SHORT TIME LATER, THE QUEEN ARRIVED.

HAIL, HIPPOLYTA, QUEEN OF THE AMAZONS!

HAIL, HERCULES, HERO OF THEBES. WHY HAVE YOU MADE THE LONG JOURNEY TO MY LAND?

BY THE GODS' WILL, I SERVE MY COUSIN, KING EURYSTHEUS OF MYCENAE.

HE HAS **COMMANDED** THAT I BRING HIM THE GOLDEN BELT YOU WEAR.

YOU PLAN TO **TAKE** IT FROM ME? DO YOU THINK I WILL NOT **FIGHT** TO KEEP IT?

IT WAS A GIFT FROM ARES, THE GOD OF WAR.

I HOPE TO **PERSUADE** YOU TO PART WITH IT. I RESPECT YOU AND YOUR WARRIORS.

I DO NOT WISH TO BE YOUR ENEMY.

HAD YOU TRIED TO **TAKE** IT, I WOULD NEVER HAVE GIVEN IT UP.

BECAUSE YOU **ASKED** AND BECAUSE OF THE RESPECT I HAVE FOR YOU AND YOUR ADVENTURES,

I WILL GIVE IT TO YOU AS A TOKEN OF FRIENDSHIP.

ONCE AGAIN, HERA WAS NEARBY, WATCHING AND HOPING THAT HERCULES WOULD FAIL. WHEN SHE SAW THE QUEEN GIVE UP THE BELT WITHOUT A FIGHT, HERA DISGUISED HERSELF AS AN AMAZON TO MAKE TROUBLE.

LOOK! HERCULES MUST HAVE TAKEN THE QUEEN **HOSTAGE!**

WHY ELSE WOULD SHE SURRENDER SUCH A TREASURE?

YES! YOU MUST BE RIGHT!

WE MUST STOP THEM BEFORE THEY SET SAIL!

STOP THEM!!

ATTACK!!!

WHAT IS THIS?!? YOU SPEAK OF **FRIENDSHIP** AND THEN YOUR WARRIORS **ATTACK?**

MY WARRIORS WOULD ONLY **ATTACK** IF THEY SAW SOME **TREACHERY!**

I SHOULD HAVE KNOWN BETTER THAN TO TRUST A **MAN!**

SAVE THE QUEEN!

STOP THEM!!

GET THEM!

NOoOOOo!!!!

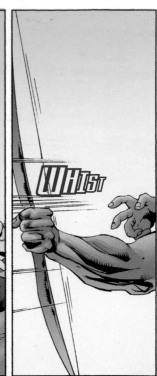

WHIST

ARrGGHHH!

YOU KILLED HIM WITH A POISONED ARROW? I AM *SURPRISED*, HERCULES.

YOU ARE A MIGHTY WARRIOR. WHY NOT FIGHT IT FAIRLY?

I THOUGHT ABOUT IT. THEN IT OCCURRED TO ME THAT YOU, YOUR CREW, AND YOUR SHIP MIGHT GET SMASHED TO PIECES IN THE FIGHT.

oh.

ABOVE AND BELOW

FOR THE *ELEVENTH LABOUR*, KING EURYSTHEUS SENT HERCULES TO BRING HIM THE GOLDEN APPLES OF THE HESPERIDES, WHICH BELONGED TO HERA. THE GODDESS WHISPERED THE SUGGESTION TO THE KING BECAUSE SHE THOUGHT THE CHALLENGE WOULD BE IMPOSSIBLE.

FIRST, EVERYONE KNEW THAT THE HESPERIDES, THE FOUR NYMPHS WHO CARED FOR THE TREE OF GOLDEN APPLES AND THE GARDEN WHERE IT GREW, GUARDED IT CAREFULLY. SECOND, NO ONE KNEW EXACTLY WHERE THE GARDEN WAS.

BUT HERCULES KNEW THAT ATLAS, THE TITAN WHO HELD UP THE SKY, WAS RELATED TO THE NYMPHS. IF ANYONE WOULD KNOW HOW TO FIND THEM, IT WOULD BE ATLAS. SO HERCULES MADE THE LONG, DANGEROUS CLIMB TO ASK HIM.

HA! I CANNOT REMEMBER THE LAST TIME SOMEONE CAME TO VISIT ME HERE.

OF COURSE, MY HOME IS NOT TOO INVITING.

WHO ARE YOU? WHY HAVE YOU COME?

I AM HERCULES. I HAVE COME FOR YOUR HELP.

I WAS TOLD TO GET SOME OF THE GOLDEN APPLES THAT THE HESPERIDES WATCH OVER.

TELL ME WHERE TO FIND THEM.

HA, HA, HA! HA! HA!

YOU LAUGH AT ME?

NO, NO. DO NOT BE ANGRY. I JUST KNOW SOME THINGS THAT YOU DO NOT.

YOU SEE, EVEN IF I TOLD YOU WHERE THE GARDEN IS AND YOU GOT PAST THE HESPERIDES, THERE IS ANOTHER OBSTACLE.

A DRAGON. SOME SAY IT HAS ONE HUNDRED HEADS. NOW, EVEN I HAVE HEARD STORIES OF YOUR STRENGTH. I KNOW YOU BEAT THE HYDRA'S NINE HEADS.

BUT ONE HUNDRED? THAT MIGHT BE TOO MUCH, EVEN FOR YOU.

LET US MAKE A BARGAIN. IF I GO TO THE GARDEN, THE HESPERIDES WILL SURELY GIVE ME SOME APPLES AND THE DRAGON WILL LET THEM.

IF YOU HOLD UP THE SKY FOR ME A WHILE, I PROMISE I WILL BRING THE APPLES HERE TO YOU.

I'M SURE YOU'RE STRONG ENOUGH.

OF COURSE I AM!

JUST EASE YOUR BACK AGAINST IT AND TAKE THE WEIGHT FROM MY SHOULDERS.

VERY GOOD. I KNEW YOU COULD MANAGE.

Umph! JUST HURRY BACK. I ...UH... NEED TO GET THOSE APPLES TO EURYSTHEUS.

OF COURSE!

OF COURSE!

EVERY HOUR THAT HE STRAINED TO HOLD THE SKY FELT LIKE A YEAR TO HERCULES. HE WAS GLAD TO SEE THE TITAN RETURN.

HERE THEY ARE! VERY PRETTY. EURYSTHEUS WILL LIKE THEM.

YES, I THINK SO TOO. NOW, TAKE BACK THE SKY.

NO. NO, I THINK NOT. I HAVE HELD THE SKY FOR LONG ENOUGH. YOU CAN HOLD IT FROM NOW ON.

REMEMBER, I PROMISED TO BRING THE APPLES HERE. I NEVER SAID I WOULD TAKE BACK THE SKY.

WHAT?!?

DO NOT WORRY. I WILL TAKE THE APPLES TO EURYSTHEUS FOR YOU.

THANK YOU FOR THAT.

YOU HAVE BEEN HOLDING THE SKY MANY YEARS. I SUPPOSE IT IS ONLY FAIR THAT SOMEONE ELSE DO IT FOR A WHILE.

I WONDER IF YOU CAN DO ME A FAVOUR, THOUGH?

CAN YOU TAKE BACK THE SKY FOR A TIME?

IF I FOLD MY CLOAK INTO A PAD FOR MY SHOULDERS I WOULD BE MORE COMFORTABLE.

HMMM. I SUPPOSE.

A PAD WOULD HAVE BEEN NICE ALL THOSE YEARS I WAS HOLDING THE SKY.

39

YOU ARE NOT DEAD.

NO, BUT I MUST GO.

JUST KNOW THAT NO ONE RETURNS FROM THE UNDERWORLD. NOT UNLESS HADES LETS HIM GO.

I KNOW.

THE MONSTROUS CERBERUS, GUARDIAN OF THE GATES OF THE UNDERWORLD, MADE SURE THAT NO ONE ESCAPED BACK INTO THE LAND OF THE LIVING.

AS HERCULES PASSED BY, HE KNEW HE MIGHT NEVER SEE THE WORLD ABOVE AGAIN.

ALONG TWISTING PATHS, HE MADE HIS WAY TO THE COURT OF HADES, LORD OF THE DEAD.

AH. I KNEW THAT A LIVING MAN HAD ENTERED MY REALM, BUT I DID NOT REALIZE THAT IT WAS YOU.

WELCOME, SON OF MY BROTHER ZEUS. WHY ARE *YOU* HERE?

I COME BECAUSE THE ORACLE AT DELPHI PUT ME IN THE SERVICE OF EURYSTHEUS.

HE COMMANDED ME TO BRING HIM CERBERUS.

DID HE? I THINK I SEE HERA'S HAND IN THIS. SHE NEVER LIKED YOU. SHE THINKS I WILL NOT LET YOU GO.

BECAUSE OF THAT, AND BECAUSE I DO NOT WANT TO ANGER ZEUS, I THINK I WILL LET YOU RETURN TO THE LAND OF THE LIVING.

THANK YOU, GREAT HADES.

WILL YOU LET ME COMPLETE MY TASK? CAN I TAKE CERBERUS WITH ME?

SINCE YOU ARE OBEYING THE ORACLE, I WILL ALLOW YOU TO TAKE CERBERUS...

BUT ONLY IF YOU CAN TAME HIM WITH YOUR BARE HANDS.

OH, AND TELL EURYSTHEUS THAT YOUR SERVICE IS AT AN END. TELL HIM I SAID SO.

GRRRRRRRRRRR

AAIIIEEEEE!

NOW, RETURN TO YOUR MASTER.

I HAVE COMPLETED THE TWELFTH LABOUR YOU GAVE ME.

NOW MY SERVICE TO YOU IS FINISHED.

THAT WAS THE END OF THE TWELVE LABOURS OF HERCULES, BUT THAT WAS NOT THE END OF HIS ADVENTURES.

ALL HIS LIFE, HERCULES NEVER STOPPED MAKING DANGEROUS JOURNEYS AND FIGHTING AGAINST FEARSOME ENEMIES, BUT THOSE ARE STORIES FOR ANOTHER TIME.

45

GLOSSARY

AMAZONS: a race of female warriors of Greek legend. Hippolyta, daughter of the god of war—Ares—is the queen of the Amazons.

ARTEMIS: the Greek goddess of the moon and of the hunt

BOAR: a wild pig

HADES: the underground dwelling place of the dead in Greek mythology

HERA: the immortal wife of Zeus

HIDE: the skin of an animal

HIND: a female deer

IMMORTAL: a being that never dies

MARE: a female horse

MORTAL: a being that dies

NYMPH: in Greek mythology, goddesses of nature who are often represented as beautiful women living in the mountains, forests, trees and waters

ORACLE: a priestess of ancient Greece through whom a god or gods were believed to speak

POSEIDON: the Greek god of the sea

TITAN: according to Greek mythology, a race of giants that ruled the earth before their overthrow by the Greek gods

ZEUS: king of the gods, father of Hercules

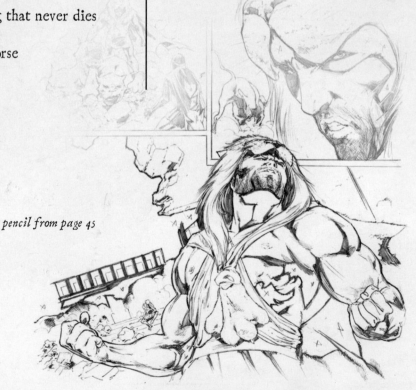

pencil from page 45

46

FURTHER READING AND WEBSITES

Greek Mythology: The Labours of Hercules
http://www.mythweb.com/hercules/index.html
> With engaging cartoons and easy-to-read text, this child-friendly site
> explores the labours of Hercules and also tells the stories of several other
> Greek heroes.

Evans, Cheryl and Anne Millard. *The Usborne Illustrated Guide to Myths and
Legends* Usborne Publishing Ltd, 1985. Identifies the gods, goddesses, heroes
and monsters of Greek mythology, recounts the most famous stories and briefly
describes Greek history and culture.

Perseus Project: Hercules: Greece's Greatest Hero
http://www.perseus.tufts.edu/Herakles/index.html
> This website from Tufts University in Massachusetts features a wealth of
> information about the legend of Hercules, including his twelve labours and
> other stories.

Philip, Neil. *Mythology* (Eyewitness Books) Dorling Kindersley Publishing, 2005.
> This volume in the Eyewitness Books series uses dozens of colourful photos
> and illustrations to explore myths from around the world.

Thomas Bulfinch: Bulfinch's Mythology
http://www.classicreader.com/booktoc.php/sid.2/bookid.2823/
> This website features one of the most popular English-language compilations
> of ancient myths. This classic work, which includes many Greek myths, was
> compiled by American Thomas Bulfinch in the 1800s.

CREATING HERCULES: THE TWELVE LABOURS

To create the story of Hercules' Twelve Labours, author Paul Storrie relied
heavily on both Thomas Bulfinch's *The Age of Fable*, first published in 1859, and
Edith Hamilton's *Mythology*, first published in 1942. Both of these drew their
material from the work of ancient poets such as Ovid and Virgil. Artist Steve
Kurth used numerous historical and traditional sources to give the art an authentic
feel, from the classical Greek architecture to the clothing, weapons and armour
worn by the characters. Together, the art and narrative text bring to life the
mightiest hero of Greek mythology, whose battles against gods and monsters
earned him a place on Mt Olympus, the home of the Greek gods.

INDEX

ABOUT THE AUTHOR AND THE ARTIST

PAUL D STORRIE was born and raised in Detroit, Michigan, USA, and has returned to live there again and again after living in other cities and states. He began writing professionally in 1987 and has written comics for Caliber Comics, Moonstone Books, Marvel Comics and DC Comics. Some of the titles he's worked on include *Robyn of Sherwood*, featuring stories about Robin Hood's daughter, *Batman Beyond*, *Gotham Girls*, *Captain America: Red, White and Blue* and *Mutant X*.

STEVE KURTH was born and raised in west central Wisconsin, USA. He graduated with a bachelor's degree in fine arts in illustration from the University of Wisconsin at Eau Claire. Steve's art has appeared in numerous comic books, including *G.I. Joe*, *Micronauts*, *Ghostbusters*, *Dragonlance* and *Cracked* magazine.